JAZZ *MEMORIES*

A Book of Days

Jerry Stoll

Michael Ehlers

This is dedicated to Tommy Flanagan, a pianist's pianist, and to the memory of John Henry Hammond [1910–1987], a jazz saint.

Unless noted all photographs are by Jerry Stoll © 1984, 1985, 1987

All text and notes by Michael Ehlers © 1987

Designed by Stephen Kruse

ISBN 0-87654-209-7

Published by Pomegranate Calendars & Books Box 808022, Petaluma, CA 94975

Printed and bound in Singapore

Photographs

Front cover:

MILES DEWEY DAVIS III (b. 1926)
Monterey Jazz Festival, 1964
"Those songs to me don't exist. We don't have time for 'Body and Soul' and 'I Got Rhythm'. Or 'So What' or 'Kind of Blue'. Those things are there. They were done in that era, the right hour, the right day. It happened and it's over. It's on the record, you know. People ask me, 'Why don't you play this?' Go buy the record! Don't like me because of 'Kind of Blue'. Like me for what I'm doing. I was put here to play music and interpret music. That's what I do. No attitude. Nothing. That's all I want to do."

Title page:

ELLA FITZGERALD (b. 1918)
Masonic Auditorium, San Francisco, 1959
Referred to by one musical associate as "unspoiled, unselfish, unaffected, and understanding," Ella Fitzgerald has for fifty years sung with precision and clarity. Like Billie Holiday, who in her best work often sang the most dreadful Tin Pan Alley potboilers, Ella can take ordinary pop songs and turn them into jazz.

Back cover:

LOUIS ARMSTRONG (1900-1971)
Monterey Jazz Festival, 1958
"One night (trumpet great) Freddie Keppard came in to hear us, and after he listened awhile, he said to Louis, 'Boy, let me have your trumpet.' So Freddie blew and blew, and the crowd gave him a nice hand. Then he handed the trumpet back to Louis. If you want to REALLY hear Louis play, just hear him play when he's angry! Boy, he blew and people started standing on top of tables and chairs screaming, and Freddie eased out real slowly. Nobody ever asked Louis for his trumpet again."
　　　　　　　—Lil Hardin (then Mrs. Armstrong)

INTRODUCTION

Jazz Memories: The Modern Jazz Quartet's exquisitely patterned compositions outdoors on a bright spring day in 1962. . . . First exposure to John Coltrane with Pharoah Sanders in concert, the most powerful and emotionally draining musical experience of my life. . . . An evening at Barron's in Harlem, Max Roach's Sextet followed by the Miles Davis Quintet. . . . Late nights at Slug's in New York's East Village, listening to Lee Morgan, or Leon Thomas, or perhaps Sun Ra's Arkestra. . . . Club 43 in Manchester, a gymnasium five days each week, but the hippest spot in northern England on weekends when Ben Webster, Rex Stewart or other visiting American jazz artists were featured.

Memories and surprises: Carmell Jones playing trumpet with a local Kansas City tavern band and sounding every bit as good as he did with Horace Silver ten years earlier. . . . Ducking into an Upper East Side singles' bar in New York to use the phone and discovering that the house pianists were Duke Jordan alternating with Al Haig. . . . Three days in heaven at the Jazz Olympics in Kansas City, a first-class event [Bösendorfer concert grand pianos] held in two ballrooms of the historic Muehlbach Hotel, where the several dozen musicians—a Who's Who of Jazz—often outnumbered the audience.

Mulling over these moments never fails to bring a smile, and it usually sends me to my turntable for audio reinforcement. Whether it is the umpteenth hearing of John Coltrane with Johnny Hartman or the latest offering from the World Saxophone Quartet, I can count on jazz, the sound of surprise, to lift my spirits or comfort me in my troubles.

This little book, too, is filled with memories, mostly those of photographer Jerry Stoll. His sensitive portraits of jazz greats capture not just the images of the musicians, but also the spirit of their music. Whether it is a pensive Miles Davis, Louis Armstrong bathed in spotlights, or the fiery Elvin Jones, Stoll's pictures go beneath the surface to a glimpse of the artist within.

Jazz artistry, though, extends beyond the musical performers. Michael Harper is a poet whose jazz verse is extraordinarily lyrical, and the mood and feel of jazz can often be found in the lines of Amiri Baraka. Jazz producers Alfred Lion of Blue Note Records fame and re-issue king Michael Coscuna of Mosaic Records are just two of the dozens who have worked tirelessly for the music. National promoters such as George Wein and countless local impresarios provide opportunities for millions of people to hear jazz. Some of our bigger cities have commercial radio stations that feature jazz, but day in and day out, all over the United States, hundreds of local public radio stations are the best friends jazz has ever had. Their programming almost always contains a good measure of jazz, often complemented by nationally syndicated shows [Marian McPartland's "Piano Jazz" or Ben Sidran's "Sidran on Record," for instance].

Writers and critics move the music along, too. James Lincoln Collier's history of jazz is recommended reading, as is the marvelously literate work of British writer Benny Green. Gary Giddens' criticism is incisive, and journalist-critic Leonard Feather brings fifty years of insight to his countless books, articles, reviews and liner notes. He authored with Ira Gitler *The Encyclopedia of Jazz in the Seventies*, perhaps the most thorough jazz reference book available. And Whitney Balliett of *The New Yorker*, armed with a boundless enthusiasm for jazz and an unmatched knowledge of its history and context, can describe the sound of music like no one else. He is as fine a chronicler as any art form could hope to inspire.

But the subject of this book is the musicians themselves. Selecting which photographs to publish was a joy. Deciding which ones to omit was agonizing. If we had had access to good shots of Lester Young and Bud Powell, they certainly would have been included. There are many others whose contributions to jazz warranted their inclusion as well, but for reasons of space, they will not be found here. Guitarists Charlie Christian and Django Reinhardt are missing, as are saxophone pioneers Frankie Trumbauer and Sidney Bechet and cornet legend Bix Beiderbecke. Saxophonists Don Byas, Phil Woods, Eric Dolphy and Theodore Walter "Sonny" Rollins belong, too. Any publication about jazz which ignores pianist Teddy Wilson is imperfect, and the pain caused by the omission of personal favorites such as altoist Sonny Stitt and baritone sax standout Pepper Adams lingers still. There are, however, only fifty-two weeks in a year, and we hope that the artists featured here with each of them will stir your own jazz memories if you are already a fan, or will inspire you to delve further into America's music.

Michael Ehlers

Introduction photograph:

JOHN BIRKS "DIZZY" GILLESPIE (b. 1917)
Backstage, Monterey Jazz Festival, 1964
"Everybody's trying to play like him. Nobody has played as much harmony on a trumpet as Dizzy. The whole conception of rhythm is Dizzy's, the whole conception of the trumpet in the upper register is Dizzy's. He's forgotton more music than I'll ever know."
—Wynton Marsalis

BILLIE HOLIDAY (1912-1959)
Monterey Jazz Festival, 1958
"She liked to come in behind the beat. To me, her greatest quality was not the one that everybody fixes on—the expression and the feeling—but her innately and absolutely perfect sense of timing. No other singer ever approached her on this."
—former Holiday accompanist Johnny Guarnieri

JANUARY

1   Louis Armstrong, age 12, sent to the Colored Waifs' Home, where he learned to play the cornet.

2

3

4

5

6

7

ELVIN RAY JONES (b. 1927)
Keystone Korner, San Francisco, 1981
Like his older brothers Hank and Thad, Elvin
Jones is a consummate musician. His work
with the John Coltrane quartet of the 1960s
is indicative of Jones' drum style—a pulsing,
churning maelstrom in which every piece of the
drum kit is used. Though weaker soloists can be
overwhelmed by Elvin's power, he is a masterful
accompanist for musicians who are his equals!

JANUARY

8 _____

9 _____
b. Kenneth Spearman "Kenny" Clark, Pittsburgh, PA (1914)

10 _____

11 _____

12 _____

13 _____

14 _____

ORNETTE COLEMAN (b. 1930)
Backstage, Monterey Jazz Festival, 1960
As Ornette Coleman has said, there is no single right way to play jazz. Critics have blasted his lack of technique, even aptitude, on the violin and trumpet (none questions his alto prowess), but it seems hard to imagine anyone unable to appreciate the rhythm, the drive, and the solid blues underpinnings of Ornette's music.

JANUARY

15

16
b. Henry Bertholf "Spike" Robinson, Kenosha, WI (1930)

17
b. Sidney Catlett, Evansville, IN (1910)

18

19

20

21

WOODROW CHARLES "WOODY" HERMAN
(b. 1913), **JOHN HALEY "ZOOT" SIMS**
(1925-1985), **SECONDO "CONTE" CANDOLI**
(b. 1927) and **RICHARD KAMUCA** (1930-1977)
Rehearsal Hall, Monterey Jazz Festival, 1959
A leader of his own bands since 1937, Woody
Herman continually has spotlighted soloists of
the first rank. With Herman are the late reed
player Richie Kamuca, trumpet stalwart Conte
Candoli and Zoot Sims, the lyrical, effortless, smooth and swinging
soprano saxophonist.

JANUARY

22
b. James Louis "J.J." Johnson, Indianapolis, IN (1924)

23

24

25

26
b. Stephane Grappelli, Paris, France (1908)

27

28

CECIL PERCIVAL TAYLOR (b. 1933)
KJAZ Festival, San Francisco, 1982
The music of new England Conservatory-trained
Cecil Taylor is so emotionally and intellectually
demanding, so complex, that it has met with a
critically and popularly mixed reaction. Classical
bass virtuoso Buell Neidlinger has said of Taylor,
"That man is capable of playing ten different
notes with ten different fingers, ten different
dynamics, ten different attacks, at ten different tempi. He is phenomenal.
There is no musician I've ever met, including Igor Stravinsky and Pierre
Boulez, who comes anywhere near having the abilities Cecil Taylor has."

JAN./FEB.

29

30
b. Roy Eldridge, Pittsburgh, PA (1911)

31

1

2
b. Edward "Sonny" Stitt, Boston, MA (1924)

3

4

WILLIAM "COUNT" BASIE (1904-1984) and
EARL KENNETH "FATHA" HINES (1903-1983)
Backstage, Monterey Jazz Festival, 1959
Basie's piano style was deceptively simple, but
he has had few equals in comping behind soloists
or in pushing a band to its limits. The hallmark of
the Basie band, a smooth, easy swing, is readily
identifiable to all but the most casual listener.
  Perhaps Basie is comparing left hands with
Earl Hines in this picture. Hines' was powerful enough to snap the strings
on a Steinway, while Basie's was one of the most understated.

FEBRUARY

5

6

7

8

9

10
b. Chick Webb, Baltimore, MD (1909)

11

JOHN CARL "JON" HENDRICKS (b. 1921) and
JOHN BIRKS "DIZZY" GILLESPIE (b. 1917)
Rehearsal, Monterey Jazz Festival, 1965
Dizzy Gillespie's playing illustrates a jazz truism:
It isn't necessary to blow hard to swing hard.
Dizzy can drop from an audible-in-the-next-block
run of 64th notes to a whispered filigreed figure.
John Hendricks (rescued from law school by an
encounter with Charlie Parker) is Dizzy's equal in articulation.
He is a tireless crusader for jazz and one of the music's greatest
vocal interpreters.

FEBRUARY

12

b. Melvin Powell, New York, NY (1923)

13

14

15

16

17

18

JOHN WILLIAM COLTRANE (1926-1967) and
PAUL LAWRENCE DUNBAR CHAMBERS
(1935-1969)

FEBRUARY

Masonic Auditorium, San Francisco, 1960
Even when he was at the height of his musical
powers, John Coltrane practiced scales in
day-long non-stop sessions. He could play with
equal power and fluency through the full range of
the tenor saxophone. Paul Chambers was part of one of the most famous
rhythm sections in jazz with drummer Philly Joe Jones and pianist Wynton
Kelly. Chambers' haunting bowed solos graced numerous recordings from
1955 until his death.

19

20

21

b. Tadley Ewing "Tadd" Dameron, Cleveland, OH (1917)

22

Village Vanguard opens in NYC (1935)

23

24

25

BENJAMIN FRANCIS "Ben" WEBSTER
(1909-1973) with **Rex Stewart** (1907-1967)
and **Benny Carter** (b. 1907)
Backstage, Monterey Jazz Festival, 1962
Ben Webster could play a ballad in the most
beautiful, lush-toned style, without ever being
schmaltzy, and then tear the house down on an
up-tempo number. His presence in the Ellington
band in the early 1940s made that orchestra
Duke's finest. Benny Carter is a Grammy-winning composer and alto
sax giant, and Rex Stewart, a trumpet star with Ellington for ten years,
was later a jazz writer of considerable talent.

FEB./MAR.

26 First jazz recording made at Victor Studios in NYC with the Original Dixieland Jass Band (1917)

27 b. Benjamin Francis Webster, Kansas City, MO (1909)

28

29

1

2

3 Cab Calloway records 'Minnie the Moocher" (first million-selling jazz record) (1931)

4

DAVID W. BRUEBECK (b. 1920) and
EUGENE JOSEPH WRIGHT (b. 1923)
Monterey Jazz Festival, 1959
In the late '50s the sinuous sound of Paul Desmond's alto saxophone and Dave Brubeck's precisely articulated piano became widely familiar. Their exploration of exotic time signatures yielded a huge commercial success *(Time Out)* and a greatly expanded audience for jazz. Compositions from that album remain Brubeck's most requested numbers, but as he says, "If a tune is good, it can withstand all that playing, and if a musician is good, he can make something new of it every time."

MARCH

5 Duke Ellington's first NYC appearance, at the Lafayette Theatre (1923)

6

7

8

9

10 b. Leon Bismarck "Bix" Beiderbecke, Davenport, IA (1903)

11

LOUIS ARMSTRONG (1900-1971)
with **Carmen McRae, Dave Brubeck,
John Lambert** and **Yolande Bavan**
"I guess it's possible there's people
who wish I'd just play like the old days
in Chicago. I say, people got all those
records and let them play 'em.

MARCH

I think when I commenced to put a little showmanship in with the music,
people appreciated me better. I got to be around great actors like Bill
Robinson. So I found out the main thing is live for that audience, live for the
public. If the people ain't sick of 'Hello Dolly', I sure ain't."

—Louis Armstrong

12 _____ d. Charles Christopher Parker, Jr., NYC (1955)

13 _____

14 _____

15 _____

16 _____

17 _____ b. Nat "King" Cole (Nathaniel Adams Coles) Montgomery, AL (1917)

18 _____

THELONIOUS SPHERE MONK (1917-1982)
Backstage, Monterey Jazz Festival, 1963
A key figure in the development of bebop in the
early '40s, Monk went in a different direction
almost at once. His lean style, utterly devoid of
ornamentation but possessed of a charming wit,
is unique in jazz. Others might know what to put
into a solo, Monk knew exactly what to leave out.
Pianists fifty years from now will be playing his
"Ruby, My Dear," "Straight No Chaser," and "'Round Midnight," and they
will have just as much trouble with them as Monk's contemporaries did.

MARCH

19   Count Basie Orchestra (with B. Holiday and J. Rushing) opens at the Apollo Theatre, NYC (1937)

20

21

22

23

24

25

OSCAR EMMANUEL PETERSON (b. 1925)
and **RAYMOND MATTHEWS BROWN**
(b. 1926)

Monterey Jazz Festival, 1959
Heir to Art Tatum's technical facility and
power, Canadian-born Oscar Peterson led a
popular trio with Ray Brown on bass and Ed
Thigpen on drums in the 1950s and '60s.
He has appeared less frequently of late
usually as a solo performer, but his keyboard pyrotechnics continue to
dazzle audiences the world over.

MAR./APR.

26

27 b. Charles Elsworth "Pee Wee" Russell, St. Louis, MO (1906)

28

29

30

31

1 b. Harry Howell Carney, Boston, MA (1910)

STANLEY GETZ (b. 1927), **JAMES ELBERT
"JIMMY" RANEY** (b. 1927) and
TOMMY WILLIAMS
Monterey Jazz Festival, 1962
Guitarist Jimmy Raney's association with Stan
Getz dates from their days with Woody Herman
in the late-'40s. Getz, one of the greatest
melody players in jazz, once said, "There are four
qualities essential to a great jazzman. They are taste, courage, individuality
and irreverence."

APRIL

2

3

4

5

6

7
b. Billie Holiday (Eleanora Fagan Gough) Baltimore, MD (1915)

8

CHARLES CHRISTOPHER PARKER, JR.
(1920-1955)
Photograph Courtesy Michael Ochs Archives, n.d.
Charlie Parker was one of the two finest
improvisers in the history of jazz (Louis
Armstrong was the other). The Art Tatum of the
alto saxophone when it came to technical ability,
"Bird" seemed able to play at the speed of light
anything in his head without even consulting his fingers. His slow blues
playing can send shivers down your spine.

APRIL

9

10   Invention of the drum, Les Eyzies, France (10,004 BC)

11

12   First extended drum solo (10,004 BC)

13

14

15

JOHN LESLIE "WES" MONTGOMERY
(1923-1968), **BARRY DOYLE HARRIS**
(b. 1929), **HAROLD DEVANCE LAND** (b. 1928)
and **RICHARD ALLEN "BLUE" MITCHELL**
(1930-1979)
Garibaldi Hall, San Francisco, 1960
Wes Montgomery made an indelible mark upon
the jazz guitar scene, despite a brief recording
career (his first record was made when he was
thirty-three) and an untimely passing. He had a full, gorgeous sound,
derived in part from his use of his thumb instead of a pick, and he was a
master of improvisation, interpreting the melody of a composition until
it was his own.

APRIL

16

17

18

19

20

21

22

b. Charles Mingus, Nogales, AZ (1922)

EARL KENNETH "FATHA" HINES
(1905-1983)
Monterey Jazz Festival, 1959
Fatha Hines brought the piano, which had been
primarily a solo instrument, into the jazz ensemble.
His career included stints with Louis Armstrong's
finest units, leadership of his own splendid big
bands, and a re-birth in the 1960s as a solo
and small group artist of the highest acclaim.

APRIL

23

24

25

26   b. Ma Rainey (Gertrude Pridgett) Columbus, GA (1886)

27

28

29   U.S. Postal Service releases Duke Ellington stamp, NYC (1986)

LIONEL HAMPTON (b. 1909) and
RICHIE COLE (b. 1948)
Monterey Jazz Festival, 1980
Lionel Hampton has had a long, eventful jazz
career, as vibraphonist with Benny Goodman's
late '30s combos, as a leader of both big and
small bands, and as one of the keenest talent
scouts anywhere. Dexter Gordon, Quincy Jones
Betty Carter, Charles Mingus and Dinah
Washington are just a few of the artists spotlighted by Hamp. Altoist
Richie Cole is a gifted but enigmatic musician who seems occasionally
torn between the influences of Charlie Parker and Victor Borge.

30 Charlie Parker's first recording date, with Jay McShann's band, NYC (1941)

1

2

3 International Tuba Day

4

5

6

ART BLAKEY (Abdullah Ibn Buhaina) (b. 1919)
U.C. Berkeley Jazz Festival, 1980
When you hear that stentorian press roll, you know it's Art Blakey and the Jazz Messengers, introducing you to the jazz stars of tomorrow. The personnel of the thirty-odd years of Messengers reads like a Who's Who of Jazz, from Horace Silver and Clifford Brown in the 1950s, through Wayne Shorter and Freddie Hubbard in the '60s, to Wynton and Branford Marsalis in the early '80s. Blakey graces several Thelonious Monk records and was perhaps the ideal drummer to complement Monk's eccentric piano style.

MAY

7

8   d. Edgar "Eddie" Jefferson, murdered in Detroit, MI (1979)

9

10

11   b. Joseph "King" Oliver, New Orleans, LA (1885)

12

13

FARRELL "PHAROAH" SANDERS
(b. 1940) and **NORMAN BISHOP**
Great American Music Hall,
San Francisco, 1980
Pharoah Sanders' emotional tenor
saxophone playing makes use of his
huge range on the instrument,
augmented by controlled "overblowing" that produces honks, squeaks
and writhing squeals. To the uninitiated, he might sound awkward, even
incoherent at times, but like Ornette Coleman and the Art Ensemble of
Chicago, Sanders' free approach is thoroughly grounded in jazz tradition.

MAY

14

15 Massey Hall concert (C. Parker, D. Gillespie, B. Powell, C. Mingus, M. Roach) Toronto, Canada (1953)

16

17

18

19

20

DEXTER KEITH GORDON (b. 1923)
Keystone Korner, San Francisco, 1981
Influenced initially by Lester Young, Dexter
Gordon became perhaps the foremost
translator of altoist Charlie Parker's magic to
the tenor saxophone in the late '40s. The genius
of his harmonic invention influenced Stan Getz,
and his complex phrasing and tonal power can be
heard in Coltrane's playing. As if this were not
enough, Gordon's spellbinding portrayal of the composite Lester
Young/Bud Powell character Dale Tuner in the 1986 film "'Round
Midnight" won him an Oscar nomination.

MAY

21
b. Thomas Wright "Fats" Waller, New York, NY (1904)

22

23

24

25
b. Miles Dewey Davis III, Alton, IL (1926)

26

27

MARY LOU WILLIAMS
(Mary Elfreida Winn) (1910-1981)
Backstage, Monterey Jazz Festival, 1965
With a career that spanned most of the history of jazz, Mary Lou Williams never stopped listening and learning. Confessor to Thelonious Monk in his early years, arranger for Basie, Ellington, and Benny Goodman, and a pianist herself of flawless technique, Williams was one of the more significant individuals in jazz.

MAY / JUNE

28

29

30   b. Benjamin David Goodman, Chicago, IL (1909)

31

1

2

3

ALFRED MCCOY TYNER (b. 1938)
U.C. Berkeley Jazz Festival, 1984
Tyner is best known for his work with John
Coltrane's mid-60s quartet, where his powerful
chording furnished the harmonic underpinnings for
Trane's saxophone flights. His playing today shows
African and Middle Eastern influences, weaving the
textures of that music into his own instrumental
and compositional style. McCoy Tyner paints
pictures and evokes moods with his music.

JUNE

4

5

6

7

8

9

10

Cotton Club of Harlem closes (1940)

HARRY HAGG JAMES (1916-1983)
Monterey Jazz Festival, 1963
James' sparkling tone on trumpet was a feature
of Benny Goodman's bands in the late '30s. Over
the next two decades he achieved considerable
commercial success with his own orchestra,
though he often played in a schmaltzy style
ill-suited to jazz. His return to the fold in the late
'50s was a welcome one for his original fans.

JUNE

11

12

13

14

15   b. Errol Louis Garner, Pittsburgh, PA (1923)

16

17

ROBERT HUTCHERSON (b. 1941) and
GEORGE ANDREW CABLES (b. 1944)
Marin City Festival, 1984
Bobby Hutcherson was the first vibraharp player
of his generation to move beyond the powerful
influence of Milt Jackson into a freer approach
to his instrument. Pianist George Cables has
recorded with Hutcherson as well as with Art
Blakey, Max Roach and Sonny Rollins.

JUNE

18

19

20   b. Eric Allan Dolphy, Los Angeles, CA (1928)

21

22   Antoine Sax, a Belgian, patents the saxophone in Paris (1846)

23 Washington Black Sox (later becoming the Duke Ellington Orchestra) open in Atlantic City, NJ (1923)

24

COLEMAN HAWKINS (1904-1969)
Rehearsal, Monterey Jazz Festival, 1963
Hawkins was pivotal in replacing the trumpet and cornet with the saxophone as the predominant solo instrument in jazz. His full, rich tone and his unparalleled melodic inventiveness have influenced generations of musicians.

JUNE / JULY

25

26   d. Clifford Brown and Richie Powell, in an auto accident on the Pennsylvania Turnpike (1956)

27

28

29

30   b. Bernard "Buddy" Rich, Brooklyn, NY (1917)

1   *down beat* magazine begins publication (1934)

JOHNNY CORNELIUS "JOHNNY"
HODGES (1906-1970) with
DUKE ELLINGTON (1899-1974)
*Backstage, Monterey Jazz Festival,
1960*
Hodges spent nearly forty years with
Ellington and made numerous small-

JULY

group recordings as well. His playing featured a sensuous tone on slower numbers and a bouncy, infectious lyricism on up-tempo pieces, "Rabbit" ranks with Charlie Parker as the most influential alto saxophonist in jazz history. Who was the better player? Neither —there couldn't be anyone better than either one.

2

3

4
b. Daniel Louis Armstrong, New Orleans, LA (1900)

5

6

7

8
b. William Clarence Eckstine, Pittsburgh, PA (1914)

SARAH LOIS VAUGHN (b. 1924)
Monterey Jazz Festival, 1980
Sarah Vaughn made her debut as an amateur
night contest winner at Harlem's Apollo Theater.
From there she came into the spotlight first with
Earl Hines' band, then Billy Eckstine's orchestra,
and later a solo career that lasts to this day.
Accepted by both pop and jazz audiences, Vaughn
possesses a rare voice which, according to musical
scholar Gunther Schuller, "...is a perfect instrument, attached to a
musician of superb instincts, capable of expressing profound human
experience."

JULY

9

10
d. Jelly Roll Morton (Ferdinand Joseph LaMenthe), Los Angeles, CA (1941)

11

12

13

14

15

ART TATUM (1910-1956)
Photograph Courtesy Michael Ochs Archives, n.d.
Art Tatum was the Fred Astaire of the piano,
playing with ease and elegance, often at blinding
tempos that would make other musicians gasp.
A recent poll of jazz pianists found over two-thirds
naming Tatum as "Most Influential Pianist."

JULY

16

17
Newport (R.I.) Jazz Festival begins (1954)

18

19

20

21
b. Conrad Yeatis "Sonny" Clark, Herminie, PA (1931)

22

HERBERT JEFFREY HANCOCK (b. 1940)
U.C. Berkeley Jazz Festival, 1983
Of the commercial success of his post-1970
music, Herbie Hancock has said: "I realized that
I could never be a genius in the class of Miles,
Charlie Parker or Coltrane, so I might just as
well forget about becoming a legend and just be
satisfied to create some music to make people
happy." He judges himself too harshly—earlier
compositions like "Maiden Voyage", "Riot" and "Dolphin Dance" will likely be
played by jazz artists for many years to come.

JULY

23

24
b. Joseph Louis Thomas, Webster Groves, MO (1909)

25

26

27

28

29
b. Donald Redman, Piedmont, W. VA (1900)

ELMER SNOWDEN (1900-1973),
GEORGE MURPHY "POPS" FOSTER
(1892-1969) and **MELVIN "TURK"**
MURPHY (1915-1987)
Backstage, Monterey Jazz Festival, 1963
Trombonist Turk Murphy was long a
fixture in traditional jazz in the San
Francisco area. He is shown here with Elmer Snowden (banjoist in Duke
Ellington's first band) and bass pioneer Pops Foster. Of Foster it has been
said, "Pops Foster may not have done a hundred and eighty miles an hour
on the superhighway. He just laid out the highway, that's all."

30 d. Jimmy Blanton, Monrovia, CA (1942)

31

1 In a conflict over record royalties, American Federation declares a ban on recording (1942-43)

2

3

4

5

HORACE WARD MARTIN TAVARES SILVER
(b. 1928), **JOSEPH A. HENDERSON** (b. 1937)
and **CARMELL JONES** (b. 1936)
Monterey Jazz Festival, 1964
From his earliest days with Stan Getz in 1950,
as a founding Messenger at the University of
Art Blakey, and as a jazz leader since the
mid-50s, Horace Silver has been a prolific
composer and an exciting, hard-driving pianist.
Many of his catchy, funk-tinged tunes have become jazz standards. Tenor
saxophonist Joe Henderson and trumpeter Carmell Jones are both former
Silver associates.

AUGUST

6

7   b. Ronald T. "Roland" Kirk, Columbus, OH (1936)

8

9

10

11

12

FREDERICK DEWAYNE HUBBARD (b. 1938)
and **ROBERT HUTCHERSON** (b. 1941)
U.C. Berkeley Jazz Festival, 1984
Freddie Hubbard has woven a circuitous
path through jazz trends. Mellow with Wes
Montgomery, avant garde with John Coltrane
and Ornette Coleman, he hit a creative peak with
his thoughtful, inspired Blue Note releases in the
1960s. His crossover success in the '70s, rife
with electronic gadgetry, drew sneers from some purists, but later
recordings with the stellar group V.S.O.P. showed Hubbard in fine
jazz form.

AUGUST

13

14

15

16

b. William John Evans, Plainfield, NJ (1929)

17

18

19

WOODROW CHARLES HERMAN
(b. 1913) and **ROY ELDRIDGE** (b. 1911)
Monterey Jazz Festival, 1959
Always a major influence on Dizzy
Gillespie, Roy "Little Jazz" Eldridge's
emotional playing, clear bright tone and
blazing high-speed runs have made him a

brass players' favorite. Clarinetist/vocalist Woody Herman has always led
exuberant bands filled with talented soloists. From the First Herd in 1944
through the spectacular Zoot Sims-Four Brothers bands and into the
present, a Herman performance has guaranteed excitement.

AUGUST

20

21
b. William "Count" Basie, Red Bank, NJ (1904)

22

23

24

25

26
b. James Andrew Rushing, Oklahoma City, OK (1903)

DINAH WASHINGTON (Ruth Jones)
(1924-1963)
Capital Studios, New York, c. 1958
Photograph by Milton J. Hinton ©
"There are all kinds of singers. Somehow, Dinah made most of the others sound like little girls. She was a woman to the core, singing of a woman's pleasures and pains. When she turned it on, she hit home. She sang what she felt and did what she pleased. She was the real thing."
  —Jazz scholar Dan Morgenstern

AUG. / SEPT.

27
b. Lester Willis Young, Woodville, MS (1909)

28

29
b. Charles Christopher Parker, Jr., Kansas City (1920)
b. Dinah Washington (Ruth Jones), Tuscaloosa, AL (1924)

30

31
Birdland opens in NYC (1949)

1

2

WILLIAM JOHN "BILL" EVANS
(1929-1980)
*Studio rehearsal, New York,
c. 1962*
Photograph by Milton J. Hinton ©
Piano virtuoso Bill Evans is named

SEPTEMBER

almost as frequently as Art Tatum when jazz pianists are asked which
players they most admire. With a left hand more melodic than rhythmic,
Evans' lyrical playing featured long, flowing lines of brilliant improvisation.
He died far too young, and the beauty and intelligence of his artistry
will be sorely missed.

3

4

5

6

7

8 Billie Holiday opens at the Famous Door (NYC) where she was forbidden to talk to patrons. (1935)

9

CEDAR ANTHONY WALTON (b. 1934) and
CURTIS DUBOIS FULLER (b. 1934)
Fantasy Studios, Berkeley, 1986
Cedar Walton is a multi-faceted pianist
whose skill as an accompanist is equalled by
his improvisational talents as a soloist. Curtis
Fuller, a former Jazz Messenger like Walton,
is another of Detroit's gifts to jazz. Fuller is
stylistic heir to the mantle of bop trombone
master J. J. Johnson and has appeared on over 300 recordings.

SEPTEMBER

10

11

12

13

14

15

16

JOHN WILLIAM COLTRANE (1926-1967)
Backstage, Monterey Jazz Festival, 1961
John Coltrane was a musician who could play
with lyrical beauty or soul-wrenching passion. Of
Coltrane's 1962 recording of the Duke Ellington
ballad "In a Sentimental Mood" long-time
Ellington sideman Johnny Hodges said, "As long
as I've known this song, I think Coltrane gave the
most beautiful interpretation I've ever heard." Critics have likened the
masterful album *A Love Supreme* (1964) to a transcendental religious
experience, with the listener borne along by the power and intensity of
the performance.

SEPTEMBER

17

18

19

20

21

22

23

b. John William Coltrane, Hamlet, NC (1926)

CHARLES MINGUS (1922-1979)
Monterey Jazz Festival, 1964
Mingus' early reputation derived mainly from
his virtuoso bass technique, documented in
some fine recordings with the Red Norvo trio
and with Bud Powell and Charlie Parker. By
the late 1950s, his ensembles began to
feature more of Mingus' own compositions,
expressionistic pieces propelled by his own
rhythmic drive and the talents of, among
others, multi-reed men Roland Kirk and Eric Dolphy, altoists Jack
McLean, Charles McPherson and John Handy, and the vastly
under-rated trombonist Jimmy Knepper.

SEPTEMBER

24

25

26
d. Bessie Smith, Clarksdale, MS (1937)

27
b. Earl "Bud" Powell, New York, NY (1924)

28

29

30
b. Oscar Pettiford, Okmulgee, OK (1922)

BETTY CARTER (b. 1930)
UC Berkeley Jazz Festival, 1980
A Betty Carter concert is a treat for both eyes and ears. She is not only a superb jazz singer, but a fine actress as well, matching the dips and swoops in her voice with her facial expressions and body movements.

OCTOBER

1

2

3
b. George Theodore Wein, Boston, MA (1925)

4

5

6

7

TOSHIKO AKIYOSHI (b. 1929) and
LEWIS BARRY TABACKIN (b. 1940)
Keystone Korner, San Francisco, 1981
Discovered and encouraged by piano virtuoso
Oscar Peterson, Toshiko Akiyoshi came to the
United States to study jazz piano at Berklee
College of Music. Her 1960s' trios and quartets
were later expanded to a big band, often
featuring the Sonny Rollins-influenced tenor saxophone of her husband,
Lew Tabackin. Akiyoshi is a prolific composer with an interest in Japanese
folk music, and she has written and arranged extensively for her band.

OCTOBER

8

b. Park "Pepper" Adams, Highland Park, IL (1930)

9

10

11

Coleman Hawkins records "Body and Soul" for Bluebird Records, NYC (1939)

12

13

b. Art Tatum, Toledo, OH (1910)

14

EDWARD KENNEDY "DUKE" ELLINGTON (1899-1974) and **WILLIAM "BILLY" STRAYHORN** (1915-1967)

Backstage, Monterey Jazz Festival, 1964
Ellington was a painter of music whose palette was his orchestra. He and his co-composer, arranger, and musical alter-ego Billy Strayhorn wrote composition after brilliant composition built around the talents and musical personalities of band members like Johnny Hodges, Bubber Miley, Ben Webster, Jimmy Blanton, Cootie Williams, Barney Bigard, and many others.

OCTOBER

15

16   b. Joe Williams (Joseph Goreed), Cordele, GA (1918)

17

18

19

20

21   b. John Birks "Dizzy" Gillespie, Cheraw, SC (1917)

BENJAMIN DAVID "BENNY" GOODMAN
(1909-1986)
Photograph courtesy Michael Ochs Archives, n.d.
Benny Goodman led a band which virtually defined swing in the mid-30s, a rare period when the popular music of America was jazz. A demanding leader who tolerated nothing but the best from his sidemen, Goodman was also a clarinetist without peer at faster tempi and a classical performer as well.

OCTOBER

22

23

24

25

26

27

28

CONNIE KAY (b. 1927) and
MAXWELL "MAX" ROACH (b. 1925)
Backstage, Monterey Jazz Festival, 1958
In his twenty-year tenure with the Modern
Jazz Quartet, Connie Kay showed just
how perfectly the term "accompanist"
could be defined. Max Roach's playing
mirrors the history of percussion
—timekeeping, accenting, driving, and even melodic at times. Whether with
Charlie Parker or Clifford Brown, leading his own quartets, or as part of
the fascinating percussion ensemble M'Boom, Roach's complex yet logical
drumming is unsurpassed.

OCT. / NOV.

29

b. John Haley "Zoot" Sims, Inglewood, CA (1925)

30

31

1

2

b. Phillip Wells Woods, Springfield, MA (1931)

3

4

NINA SIMONE (Eunice Waymon) (b. 1933)
Masonic Auditorium, San Francisco, 1960
Nina Simone's evocative voice is equally
comfortable with ballads or gospel, folk
songs or pop songs. With just the spin
of a turntable, her dusky blues stylings
can transport the listener to that rainy
night in a lonely place.

NOVEMBER

5

6

7

8

9

10

11

b. Wilbur "Buck" Clayton, Parsons, KS (1911)

WELDON LEO "JACK"
TEAGARDEN (1905-1964) with
his mother and **NORMA** and
CHARLIE TEAGARDEN
*Backstage, Monterey Jazz
Festival, 1963*
As a trombonist, Teagarden
played Dixieland and blues with equal facility. Even if he had never played
an instrument, however, he would be remembered for his singing, a
legato baritone with the languid, after-the-beat timing of Billie Holiday.

NOVEMBER

12 Louis Armstrong records his first Hot Five and Hot Seven sides for Okeh Records in Chicago (1925)

13

14

15

16

17

18

DAVID ALDEN LAMBERT (1917-1966), **"JON" HENDRICKS** (b. 1921), **CHARLES E. "IKE" ISAACS** (b. 1923) and **ANNIE ROSS** with **GILDO MAHONES** (b. 1929) Dave Lambert and Jon Hendricks, with Annie Ross, extended Eddie Jefferson's concept of vocalese

NOVEMBER

—writing lyrics to established jazz solos—into another dimension, evidenced by the 1958 landmark recording of the solos of the entire Basie Band *(Sing a Song of Basie)*. Lambert's voice was stilled by an automobile accident in 1966, but Jon Hendricks remains one of the swingingest jazz singers ever.

19

20

21 Coleman Hawkins gets his first saxophone on his 9th birthday (1913)

22

23

24

25 b. Williams Henry Joseph Berthol Bonaparte Bertholoff "Willie the Lion" Smith, Goshen, NY (1897)

FRANK MORGAN (b. 1933), **EDDIE MARSHALL** (b. 1938), **LAURIE ANTONELLI** and **JAMES LEWIS**
Studio 552, Oakland, 1987
Altoist Frank Morgan has returned only recently to the jazz scene after a three-decade battle with drug addiction. His playing today, very much in the Parker tradition, is vibrant and resourceful, and his career seems at last pointed in the direction of wider recognition and reward.

26

27

28

29

30

1

2

JOHN AARON LEWIS (b. 1920)
Backstage, Monterey Jazz Festival, 1959
Finding his inspiration in the form and structure of European classical music, Lewis, with the Modern Jazz Quartet, began in the 1950s to explore new territory in jazz. His spare piano style was complemented beautifully by the full, bluesy sound of vibraphonist Milt Jackson and was supported by bassist Percy Heath and drummers Kenny Clarke and later, Connie Kay.

DECEMBER

3

4

5

Repeal of Prohibition effective (1933)

6

7

8

9

HELEN HUMES (1913-1981)
Monterey Jazz Festival, 1980
Helen Humes first came to prominence with the Count Basie band in the late '30s when she replaced Billie Holiday. Her clear, light, at times girlish voice was, in fact, somewhat reminiscent of Holiday in her early recordings. Humes' horn-like phrasing, precise diction and stage presence are qualities which many of today's singers would do well to study.

DECEMBER

10

11

12

13

14
b. Clark Terry, St. Louis, MO (1920)

15
b. John Henry Hammond, Jr., New York, NY (1910)

16

**CHARLES ELSWORTH "PEE WEE"
RUSSELL** (1906-1969) and
**GERALD JOSEPH "GERRY"
MULLIGAN** (b. 1927)
*Backstage, Monterey Jazz Festival,
1963*

DECEMBER

Baritone saxophonist Gerry Mulligan
is a master of this difficult instrument,
with an especially elegant tone at the higher end of the horn's range.
Clarinetist extraordinaire Pee Wee Russell had an unorthodox,
introspective style—sometimes growling, at times legato—which he
played in an almost flat tone, and which remains unique in jazz today.

17

18   b. Fletcher Hamilton Henderson, Jr., Cuthbert, GA (1898)

19

20

21

22   Modern Jazz Quartet begins its recording career (Prestige Records), NYC (1952)

23   "Spirituals to Swing" concert, Carnegie Hall, NYC (1938)

JULIAN EDWIN "CANNONBALL" ADDERLEY
(1928-1975) and **NATHANIEL "NAT" ADDERLEY** (b. 1931)

Backstage, Monterey Jazz Festival, 1960
Enthusiastic, hard-blowing alto saxophonist Cannonball Adderley came to the fore with Miles Davis in the mid-50s. His later ensembles, often with his brother Nat on cornet, made use of popular funk styles to expand jazz horizons and audiences. Cannonball was active in music education and humanitarian causes, and he also wrote for movies, hosted a television program and composed a musical based upon the legend of John Henry.

DECEMBER

24

25

b. Edward "Kid" Ory, La Place, LA (1886)

26

27

28

b. Earl Kenneth "Fatha" Hines, Duquesne, PA (1905)

29

30   ## 31